Have you heard...

Illustrated by Dianne Stuchbury

A LITTLE LION
Oxford · Batavia · Sydney

songbirds whistling

woodpeckers tapping

insects humming

grasses whispering

leaves fluttering

raindrops pattering

hail drumming

thunder crashing

water gurgling

fish splashing?

Do you sometimes join in

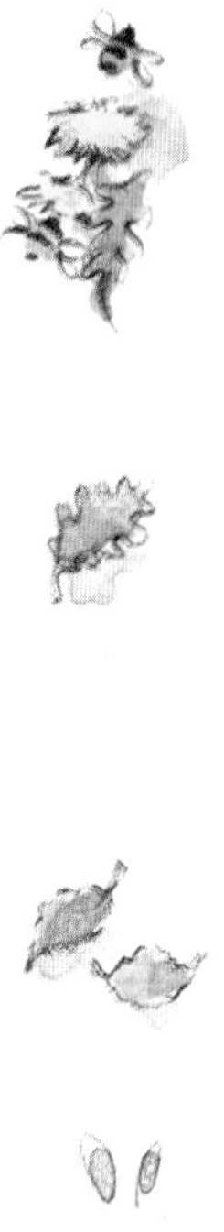

with all the sounds around you?

Dear God,
when I hear the music in your world
I want to sing and dance
for joy.

Published by
Lion Publishing plc
Sandy Lane West, Oxford, England
ISBN 0 7459 2001 2
Lion Publishing Corporation
1705 Hubbard Avenue, Batavia, Illinois 60510, USA
ISBN 0 7459 2001 2
Albatross Books Pty Ltd
PO Box 320, Sutherland, NSW 2232, Australia
ISBN 0 7324 0298 0

First published 1991

Printed and bound in Yugoslavia